AN UNOFFICIAL GRAPHIC NOVEL
FOR MINECRAFTERS

REVENGE *of the* ZOMBIE MONKS

CARA J. STEVENS
ART BY **DAVID NORGREN**
AND **ELIAS NORGREN**

ISBN 978-1-338-13059-1

The publisher does not have any control over and does not assume any responsibility for author or third-party websites or their content.

12 11 10 9 8 7 6 5 4 3 2 1   16 17 18 19 20 21

Printed in the U.S.A.   40

First Scholastic printing, September 2016

Special thanks to Cara J. Stevens, David Norgren, and Elias Norgren.

Cover design by Brian Peterson
Cover illustration credit Bethany Straker

Editor: Julie Matysik
Designer: Joshua Barnaby

INTRODUCTION

If you have played Minecraft, then you know all about Minecraft worlds. They're made of blocks you can mine: coal, dirt, and sand. In the game, you'll find many different creatures, lands, and villages inhabited by strange villagers with bald heads. The villagers who live there have their own special, magical worlds that are protected by a string of border worlds to stop outsiders from finding them.

When we last left the small border world of Xenos, Phoenix had to leave home to protect her village from her secret identity as an outsider. T.H., a mischievous hermit boy, offered her the protection of his hut until she could safely return. Unfortunately, the monks protecting the border world had been turned into zombies, leaving Xenos and all its inhabitants unprotected.

Our story resumes as these two young friends are about to set out on a journey to avenge the monks and save their peaceful world from destruction.

CHAPTER 1

THE HUT

CHAPTER 2

THE WITCH

CHAPTER 3

THE
DEEP DF

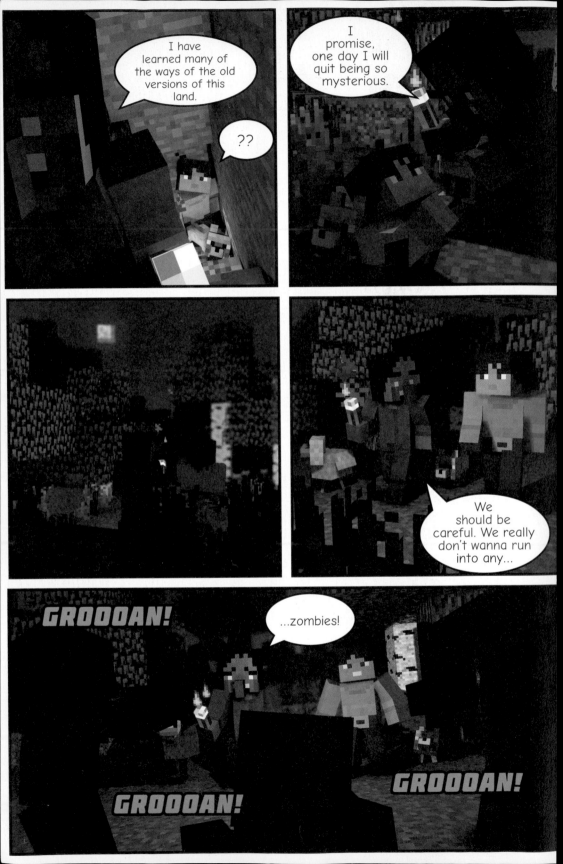

CHAPTER 4

SHELTER

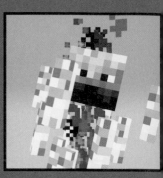

CHAPTER 5

THE TEMPLE

Gee, I almost feel bad for her. But why did she want to capture me the first time we met?

So she could prove there's a miner living in a village world. If she could prove you exist, the master librarians would decide Xenos isn't safe anymore. Then the librarians would be forced to convert Xenos to a miner world, making the land an all-you-can-eat buffet of miners for the witch...and she'd be free to leave.

⸓Cluuuck!⸓

Is there any way to cure a witch? She can't be happy being a witch. It seems kind of lonely.

Hmm... if you splash a witch with weakness potion then feed her an enchanted apple...it just might work.

Hey, look, I think we found a temple!

I wonder who built it and why.

CLATTER

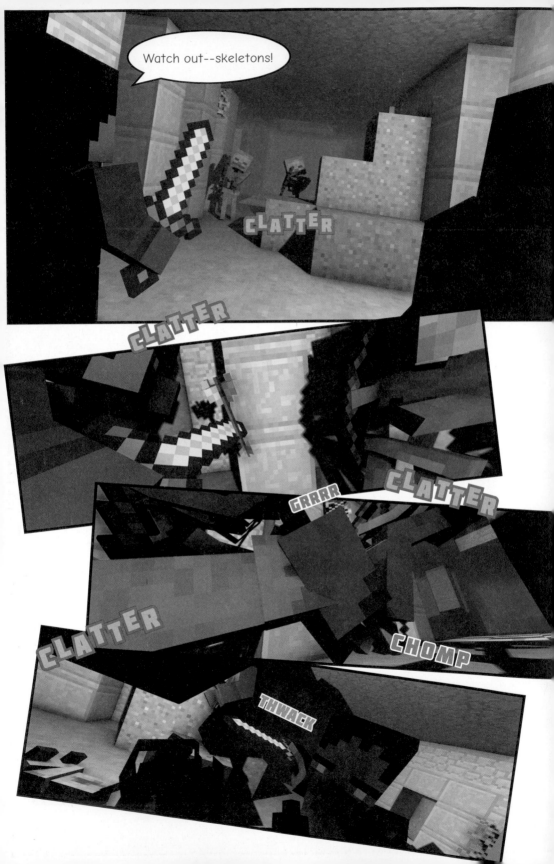

So, these temples are abandoned, huh? You forgot to mention the hostile skeletons.

Did not.

Did too.

Did not.

Did too.

Sheesh!

The temples have been abandoned by the people who built them and have been protected by hostile mobs for as long as anyone can remember. But there are still treasure chests hidden around here.

Do you know what's in them?

I've heard that there are diamonds in the chests. I could really use those for some serious mob-slaying, hut-building, and major-farming tools.

Thank you.

You're a very practical guy, T.H.

I'm not sure I meant that as a compliment.

CHAPTER 6

CHAPTER 7

ABANDONED

CHAPTER 8

DARKNESS

She was my
person first.

I'm
younger and
cuter. And
smaller.

I saved her life.
So there.

CHAPTER 9

THE CAVE OF DIAMONDS

CHAPTER 10

THE AMULET

An Eye of Ender, enchanted or not, will show the way to a stronghold. If there is a stronghold nearby, we must seek it out.

What's a stronghold?

Sigh. Really?

Something I should have learned in school?

Yes, Phoenix. A stronghold is a magical, strange place. It's an adventurer's dream, really. Some say strongholds are abandoned underground castles.

ZAP!

KA-BOOM!

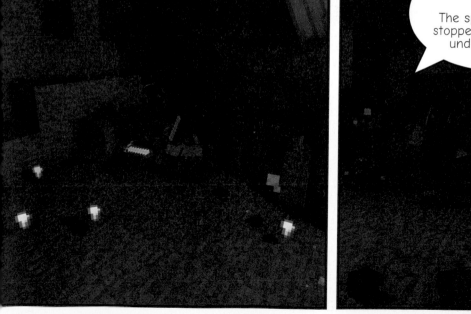

The sparkles stopped. I don't understand.

CHAPTER 11

THE STRONGHOLD

CHAPTER 12

THE MOUNTAIN OF XENOS

CHAPTER 13

ZOMBIES NO MORE